CHESTER'S EASIEST
CHRISTMAS MUSIC

Seventeen songs & piano solos for Christmas
by Carol Barratt

This book is dedicated to Ann and Tom Barratt - enjoy yourselves!

The chord symbols suggested have been chosen to suit the solo melody and
do not always correspond with the harmony of the arrangements, as importance has been
placed on interesting left hand accompaniments using simple hand positions.

This book © Copyright 1994 Chester Music
Order No. CH60144. ISBN 0-7119-4310-9

Illustrations by Sarah Lenton
© 1994 Sarah Lenton.

Music processed by Barnes Music Engraving.
Printed in the United Kingdom by Caligraving Limited, Thetford, Norfolk.

Chester Music Limited
(A division of Music Sales Limited)
14/15 Berners Street, London W1T 3LJ

PAT-A-PAN

The *staccato* notes in the left hand are important as they imitate the sound of the drum, or tambourin*, which would have accompanied this ancient French Carol.

Moderately – not fast

Burgundian Traditional Carol

* The tambourin was a small elongated drum which hung from the shoulders. It was originally played with the hands.

GO, TELL IT ON THE MOUNTAIN

American Traditional

CHRISTMAS PASTORALE

Valentin Rathgeber
(1682 – 1750)

CHRISTMAS IS COMING

English Traditional

WHAT SHALL I GIVE TO THE CHILD IN THE MANGER?

Words: Angela Diller and Kate Stearn-Page

Music: Spanish Carol

2. What shall I give to the child in the manger?
What shall I give to the beautiful boy?
Garlands of flowers to twine in his fingers,
Cherries so big for the child to enjoy.
Tam-pa-tam-tam when the cherries have ripened,
Tam-pa-tam-tam they will add to his joy.

Words from A Christmas Carol Pagent by Angela Diller and Kate Stearn-Page
© Copyright 1950 (Renewed) by G. Schirmer, Inc.

GATHERED ROUND
THE CHRISTMAS TREE

**Adapted from
Vladimir Rebikov
(1866 – 1920)**

✛ = Coda Sign: Second time round, jump from this sign to the same sign at the end of the piece to complete the music.

IL EST NÉ

French Traditional Carol

*If you are learning how to use the sustaining pedal, this piece would be ideal for practising 'legato' pedalling to give a fuller sound to the chords.

Variation on an old English Carol
I SAW THREE SHIPS

Bring out the tune in the top half of your right hand, listening carefully to the balance between the parts.

Carol Barratt

* Change the pedal every half bar ie.
(Bars 1 and 2, whole bar for each pedal)

THE LITTLE DRUMMER BOY

Words: Katherine K. Davis

Czech Carol Tune

Rhythmically

To lay be - fore the king, pa - rum pum pum pum, rum pum pum pum,

F   B♭   F7   B♭   F

rum pum pum pum._____   So   to   hon-our him, pa -

F

- rum pum pum pum,_____   When we come._____

C7   F   C7   F

JINGLE BELLS

James Pierpont

THE VIRGIN MARY HAD A BABY BOY

West Indian Spiritual

2. The angels sang when the baby born,
   The angels sang when the baby born,
   The angels sang when the baby born,
   And proclaimed him the Saviour Jesus.
   He came from the glory...

3. The wise men saw where the baby born,
   The wise men saw where the baby born,
   The wise men saw where the baby born,
   And they say that his name was Jesus.
   He came from the glory...

JUST ANOTHER STAR

Carol Barratt
Karl Jenkins

2. Just another candle in the night,
Just another shelter out of sight,
Just another shepherd passin' by,
Sheep stood round the manger listenin' to a lullaby.
It was such a special place to stay,
It was such a happy Christmas Day,
It was such a glowing star that shone
Up above the stable, where the Holy Child was born.
Love isn't ever far...

SLEIGH RIDE

Adapted from Czerny's piano reduction of a German Dance for Orchestra (K.605) by
Wolfgang Amadeus Mozart (1756 – 91).

A STARRY NIGHT

Words and music:
Joy Webb

2. Soon the shepherds came that way
Where the baby lay
And were kneeling, kneeling by his side,
And their hearts believed again
For the peace of men,
For a boy was born King of all the world.
And all the angels sang for him . . .

WHEN SANTA GOT STUCK UP THE CHIMNEY

**Words and music by
Jimmy Grafton**

Very steadily – not fast

CHRISTMAS CARILLON

Carol Barratt

AS I SAT ON A SUNNY BANK

Words: Traditional   **Music: Carol Barratt**

With a lilt – Fairly slow

mp

As I sat on a sun - ny bank on

Christ - mas Day in the morn - ing,___ I spied three ships come

sail - ing by on Christ - mas Day in the morn - ing;___ And

who should be with those three ships But Jo - seph and his fair

This **D** can be omitted if
turning the page yourself.